Introductory | Book 4

What's Next?

A Multilevel Phonics Approach for ESL Students

D1283876

Lia Conklin

New Readers Press
ProLiteracy's publishing division

What's Next? Introductory Book 4
ISBN 978-1-56420-960-3

Copyright © 2012 New Readers Press
New Readers Press
A Publishing Division of ProLiteracy
104 Marcellus Street, Syracuse, New York 13204
www.newreaderspress.com

Printed in the United States of America
9 8 7 6 5 4 3 2

Proceeds from the sale of New Readers Press materials support professional
development, training, and technical assistance programs of ProLiteracy
that benefit local literacy programs in the U.S. and around the globe.

Editorial Director: Terrie Lipke
Developmental Editor: Tracy Carman
Design and Production Director: James P. Wallace
Production Specialist: Maryellen Casey
Senior Designer: Carolyn Wallace
Illustrations: Craig Phillips

Contents

Apartment Problems

Long *i: i_e*

Samsam and Adam don't
like their apartment.

It is in a nice location, but
it has many problems.

Samsam is cooking rice,
but the stove is broken.

Adam is washing dishes, but
the pipes are leaking.

At night, they hear mice running in the walls.

They told their landlord about the problems a while ago.

They are tired of waiting for him.

Maybe they will write a letter of complaint.

Or maybe it is time to find a new apartment.

What will Samsam and Adam decide to do?

Reading Comprehension: Circle *Yes* or *No*.

1. Samsam likes her apartment.  **Yes** **No**

2. Their apartment is in a nice place.  **Yes** **No**

3. The stove needs to be fixed. 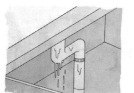 **Yes** **No**

4. Water is leaking in the kitchen.  **Yes** **No**

5. They told their landlord yesterday.  **Yes** **No**

6. The landlord fixed the problems.  **Yes** **No**

7. Maybe they will move.  **Yes** **No**

Circle the picture.

8. What will Samsam and Adam decide to do?

Sentence Practice

Part 1: Trace the long *i: i_e* words. Copy each sentence.

decide	mice	rice	pipes	like
write	time	nice	while	tired

1. Samsam and Adam don't like their apartment.

   Samsam and Adam don't like their apartment.

2. It is in a nice location, but it has many problems.

   _____

3. Samsam is cooking rice, but the stove is broken.

   _____

4. Adam is washing dishes, but the pipes are leaking.

   _____

5. At night, they hear mice running in the walls.

   _____

6. They told their landlord about the problems a while ago.

   _____

7. They are tired of waiting for him.

   _____

8. Maybe they will write a letter of complaint.

   _____

9. Or maybe it is time to find a new apartment.

   _____

10. What will Samsam and Adam decide to do?

   _____

Part 2: Trace the sight words. Copy each sentence.

| what | washing | apartment | maybe | find |
| broken | waiting | about | problems | running |

1. Samsam and Adam don't like their apartment.

   Samsam and Adam don't like their apartment.

2. It is in a nice location, but it has many problems.

   _____

3. Right now, Samsam is cooking rice, but the stove is broken.

   _____

4. Adam is washing dishes, but the pipes are leaking.

   _____

5. At night, they hear mice running in the walls.

   _____

6. They told their landlord about the problems a while ago.

   _____

7. They are tired of waiting for him.

   _____

8. Maybe they will write a letter of complaint.

   _____

9. Or maybe it is time to find a new apartment.

   _____

10. What will Samsam and Adam decide to do?

    _____

Listening Quizzes
Part 1: Letter Sounds: Listen and write the missing letters.

1. m_____c_____

2. r_____c_____

3. t_____m_____

4. wh_____l_____

5. t_____r_____d

6. n_____c_____

7. _____i_____e

8. _____i_____e

9. _____i_____e

10. _____i_____e

11. _____i_____e

12. _____i_____es

Part 2: Word Families: Listen and write the long *i: i_e* words.

1. _____

2. _____

3. _____

4. _____

5. _____

6. _____

Part 3: Sound Match: Listen and circle the words you hear.

1. mice   miss   mess

2. Tim   time   team

3. will   while   well

4. fine   fin   fan

5. lake   like   lick

6. Russ   race   rice

Part 4: Sight Words: Listen and write the sight words.

1. _____

2. _____

3. _____

4. _____

5. _____

6. _____

7. _____

8. _____

9. _____

10. _____

Part 5: Dictation: Listen and complete the sentences.

1. Samsam and Adam don't _____ their _____.

2. It is in a _____ location, but it has many _____.

3. Samsam is cooking _____, but the stove is _____.

4. Adam is _____ dishes, but the _____ are leaking.

5. They told their landlord _____ the problems a _____ ago.

6. They are _____ of _____ for him.

7. _____ they will _____ a letter of complaint.

8. _____ will Samsam and Adam _____ to do?

Apartment Search

Long *i: igh*

Samsam and Adam decided
not to fight their landlord.

Right now, they are looking
at ads in the newspaper.

APARTMENTS

Apt. for Rent. Lg. 2bd, 2 bath
nr lake. Util. not incl. $1250.

Apt. for Rent. Lg. 3bd, 2 bath
nr lake. Fireplace, util. incl.
$1500.

Apt. for Rent. Nice 2bd, 2 bath
Mod. kit. AC. Util. not incl.
$1400.

There are many apartments,
but most have high rent.

This two bedroom
looks all right.

APARTMENTS

Apt. for Rent. 2bd, 1 bath,
$750, util. incl. Call (555)
634-4444 for appt.

"This two bedroom looks
all right," Samsam says.

"Let's make an appointment to see it tonight," Adam agrees.

The apartment is a welcome sight.

There are two large bedrooms that are clean and bright.

There is a beautiful light in the kitchen.

The utilities are included, and the price is right.

What might Samsam and Adam do next?

Reading Comprehension: Circle *Yes* or *No*.

1. Samsam and Adam are looking for a house.

Yes   No

2. There are many apartments for rent.

Yes   No

3. Most of the apartments have low rent.

Yes   No

4. They visit a one-bedroom apartment.

Yes   No

5. There is a beautiful light in the bathroom.

Yes   No

6. The renter needs to pay the utilities.

Yes   No

7. The price is good for Samsam and Adam.

Yes   No

Circle the picture.

8. What might Samsam and Adam do next?

Sentence Practice

Part 1: Trace the long *i: igh* word. Copy each sentence.

right	right	light	bright	sight
tonight	high	fight	right	might

1. Samsam and Adam decided not to fight their landlord.

   Samsam and Adam decided not to fight their landlord.

2. Right now, they are looking at ads in the newspaper.

   _____

3. There are many apartments, but most have high rent.

   _____

4. "This two bedroom looks all right," Samsam says.

   _____

5. "Let's make an appointment to see it tonight," Adam agrees.

   _____

6. The apartment is a welcome sight.

   _____

7. There are two large bedrooms that are clean and bright.

   _____

8. There is a beautiful light in the kitchen.

   _____

9. The utilities are included, and the price is right.

   _____

10. What might Samsam and Adam do next?

    _____

Part 2: Trace the sight words. Copy each sentence.

landlord	next	appointment	there is	there are
welcome	most	newspaper	bedroom	price

1. Samsam and Adam decided not to fight their landlord.

   Samsam and Adam decided not to fight their landlord.

2. Right now, they are looking at ads in the newspaper.

   _____

3. There are many apartments, but most have high rent.

   _____

4. "This two bedroom looks all right," Samsam says.

   _____

5. "Let's make an appointment to see it tonight," Adam agrees.

   _____

6. The apartment is a welcome sight.

   _____

7. There are two large bedrooms that are clean and bright.

   _____

8. There is a beautiful light in the kitchen.

   _____

9. The utilities are included, and the price is right.

   _____

10. What might Samsam and Adam do next?

   _____

16   Lesson 2:   Apartment Search

Listening Quizzes
Part 1: Letter Sounds: Listen and write the missing letters.

1. m_____t

2. l_____t

3. s_____t

4. r_____t

5. h_____

6. f_____t

7. _____igh_____

8. _____igh_____

9. _____igh_____

10. _____igh

11. _____igh_____

12. _____igh_____

Part 2: Word Families: Listen and write the long *i: igh* words.

1. _____

2. _____

3. _____

4. _____

5. _____

6. _____

Part 3: Sound Match: Listen and circle the words you hear.

1. mitt   might   mat

2. sight   sat   sit

3. fat   feet   fight

4. light   lit   let

5. say   sigh   see

6. rate   wrote   right

Part 4: Sight Words: Listen and write the sight words.

1. _____

2. _____

3. _____

4. _____

5. _____

6. _____

7. _____

8. _____

9. _____

10. _____

Part 5: Dictation: Listen and complete the sentences.

1. Samsam and Adam decided not to _____ their

   _____.

2. _____ now, they are looking at ads in the _____.

3. "This two _____ looks all _____," Samsam says.

4. "Let's make an _____ to see it _____," Adam

   agrees.

5. The apartment is a _____ _____.

6. _____ _____ two large bedrooms that are clean

   and _____.

7. The utilities are included, and the _____ is _____.

8. What _____ Samsam and Adam do _____?

LESSON 3:

Samsam's Doctor's Appointment

Long *o*: *oa*, *ow*

Samsam wakes up with a moan.

She feels sick like she is on a boat.

She throws up the goat
meat she ate last night.

She calls the clinic and grabs her coat.

At her appointment, she shows her insurance card.

She fills out each row on the medical history form.

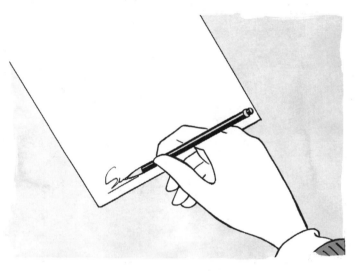

She signs her name below.

Then the doctor wants to know about her symptoms.

"I think I know what's wrong," the doctor says.

What will Samsam's test results show?

Reading Comprehension: Circle *Yes* or *No*.

1. Samsam feels sick.

Yes   **No**

2. She makes an appointment.

Yes   **No**

3. She shows her credit card at the clinic.

Yes   **No**

4. She fills out a medical history form.

Yes   **No**

5. She writes her signature on the form.

Yes   **No**

6. The doctor asks her about her medical history.

Yes   **No**

7. The doctor doesn't know what is wrong.

Yes   **No**

Circle the picture.

8. What will Samsam's test results show?

Sentence Practice

Part 1: Trace the long *o: oa, ow* words. Copy each sentence.

show	boat	throws	below	know	coat
shows	moan	goat	row	know	

1. Samsam wakes up with a moan.

   <u>Samsam wakes up with a moan.</u>

2. She feels sick like she is on a boat.

   _____

3. She throws up the goat meat she ate last night.

   _____

4. She calls the clinic and grabs her coat.

   _____

5. At her appointment, she shows her insurance card.

   _____

6. She fills out each row on the medical history form.

   _____

7. She signs her name below.

   _____

8. Then the doctor wants to know about her symptoms.

   _____

9. "I think I know what's wrong," the doctor says.

   _____

10. What will Samsam's test results show?

    _____

Part 2: Trace the sight words. Copy each sentence.

doctor	wrong	wakes up	clinic	form
ate	signs	appointment	feels	results

1. Samsam wakes up with a moan.

   <u>Samsam wakes up with a moan.</u>

2. She feels sick like she is on a boat.

   _____

3. She throws up the goat meat she ate last night.

   _____

4. She calls the clinic and grabs her coat.

   _____

5. At her appointment, she shows her insurance card.

   _____

6. She fills out each row on the medical history form.

   _____

7. She signs her name below.

   _____

8. Then the doctor wants to know about her symptoms.

   _____

9. "I think I know what's wrong," the doctor says.

   _____

10. What will Samsam's test results show?

    _____

Listening Quizzes

Part 1: Letter Sounds: Listen and write the missing letters.

1. m_____n

2. c_____t

3. kn_____

4. sh_____

5. g_____t

6. bel_____

7. _____ow

8. _____oa_____

9. _____oa_____

10. _____ow

11. _____oa_____

12. _____ow

Part 2: Word Families: Listen and write the long *o: oa* or *ow* words.

1. _____

2. _____

3. _____

4. _____

5. _____

6. _____

Part 3: Sound Match: Listen and circle the word you hear.

1. moan   man   mean

2. cat   coat   cut

3. got   goat   get

4. she   shy   show

5. know   knee   not

6. low   lie   lay

Part 4: Sight Words: Listen and write the sight words.

1. _____

2. _____

3. _____

4. _____

5. _____

6. _____

7. _____

8. _____

9. _____

10. _____

Part 5: Dictation: Listen and complete the sentences.

1. Samsam _____ _____ with a _____.

2. She _____ up the _____ meat she _____ last night.

3. At her _____, she _____ her insurance card.

4. She fills out each _____ on the medical history _____.

5. She _____ her name _____.

6. Then the _____ wants to _____ about her symptoms.

7. "I think I _____ what's _____," the doctor says.

8. What will Samsam's test _____ _____?

LESSON 4:

Doctor's Orders

Long o: o_e, ow

The doctor shows Samsam
the test results.

Samsam doesn't feel as sick anymore.

She feels hope!

"You'll feel sick a couple more
months," the doctor says.

"You should eat more fruits and vegetables."

"You shouldn't smoke or drink alcohol or coffee."

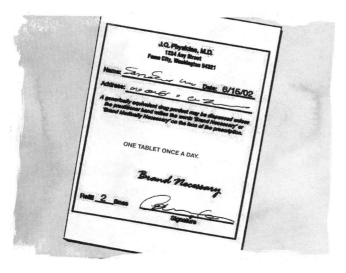

The doctor gives her a note, or prescription, for vitamins.

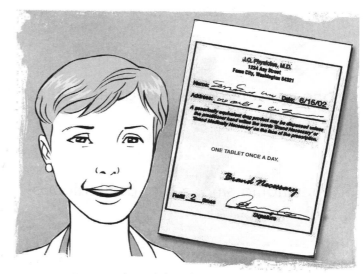

"You should take one dose once a day," she says.

Samsam can't wait to get home to use the phone.

Who will she call on the phone?

Reading Comprehension: Circle *Yes* or *No*.

1. The doctor shows Samsam why she is sick.  **Yes** **No**

2. Samsam feels a little better.  **Yes** **No**

3. The doctor says she'll feel sick a couple more days.  **Yes** **No**

4. She should eat fruits and vegetables.  **Yes** **No**

5. She should smoke and drink alcohol.  **Yes** **No**

6. Samsam gets a prescription for medicine.  **Yes** **No**

7. She should take one dose twice a day.  **Yes** **No**

Circle the picture.

8. Who will she call on the phone?

Sentence Practice

Part 1: Trace the long *o: o_e, ow* words. Copy each sentence.

shows	more	hope	home	dose
note	more	smoke	phone	anymore

1. The doctor shows Samsam the test results.

   The doctor shows Samsam the test results.

2. Samsam doesn't feel as sick anymore.

   _____

3. She feels hope!

   _____

4. "You'll feel sick a couple more months," the doctor says.

   _____

5. "You should eat more fruits and vegetables."

   _____

6. "You shouldn't smoke or drink alcohol or coffee."

   _____

7. The doctor gives her a note, or prescription, for vitamins.

   _____

8. "You should take one dose once a day," she says.

   _____

9. Samsam can't wait to get home to use the phone.

   _____

10. Who will she call on the phone?

   _____

Part 2: Trace the sight words. Copy each sentence.

who	doesn't	should	once	can't
gives	feels	shouldn't	months	results

1. The doctor shows Samsam the test results.

   The doctor shows Samsam the test results.

2. Samsam doesn't feel as sick anymore.

   _____

3. She feels hope!

   _____

4. "You'll feel sick a couple more months," the doctor says.

   _____

5. "You should eat more fruits and vegetables."

   _____

6. "You shouldn't smoke or drink alcohol or coffee."

   _____

7. The doctor gives her a note, or prescription, for vitamins.

   _____

8. "You should take one dose once a day," she says.

   _____

9. Samsam can't wait to get home to use the phone.

   _____

10. Who will she call on the phone?

    _____

Listening Quizzes
Part 1: Letter Sounds: Listen and write the missing letters.

1. m_____r_____

2. sh_____s

3. h_____p_____

4. h_____m_____

5. sm_____k_____

6. d_____s_____

7. _____o_____e

8. _____o_____e

9. _____o_____e

10. _____ows

11. _____o_____e

12. _____o_____e

Part 2: Word Families: Listen and write the long o: o_e words.

1. _____

2. _____

3. _____

4. _____

5. _____

6. _____

Part 3: Sound Match: Listen and circle the words you hear.

1. home   him   ham

2. know   knee   knew

3. phone   fun   fan

4. she   shy   show

5. note   night   not

6. hope   hop   hip

Part 4: Sight Words: Listen and write the sight words.

1. _____

2. _____

3. _____

4. _____

5. _____

6. _____

7. _____

8. _____

9. _____

10. _____

Part 5: Dictation: Listen and complete the sentences.

1. The doctor _____ Samsam the test _____.

2. Samsam _____ feel as sick _____.

3. "You'll feel sick a couple _____ _____,"
   the doctor says.

4. "You _____ eat _____ fruits and vegetables."

5. "You _____ _____ or drink alcohol or coffee."

6. "You should take one _____ _____ a day,"
   she says.

7. Samsam _____ wait to get _____ to use the phone.

8. _____ will she call on the _____?

Samsam's Surprise

Long *u*: *u_e, ue, ew*

Samsam calls her husband, Ahmed, with the news.

"What's new?" Ahmed asks.

"I'll give you a clue," Samsam says.

"What's cute and little and wears pink or blue?"

Ahmed doesn't know the American rule for pink or blue.

"I'm pregnant and due in a few months!" Samsam says.

"Is that true?" Ahmed asks, surprised.

"Yes, it's true."

"What do you want, pink or blue?"

What do the colors pink and blue mean?

Reading Comprehension: Circle *Yes* or *No*.

1. Samsam calls her father.  Yes   No

2. She asks him what wears pink or blue.  Yes   No

3. Ahmed knows the American custom.  Yes   No

4. Samsam is pregnant.  Yes   No

5. Samsam will have the baby in a few months.  Yes   No

6. Ahmed is surprised.  Yes   No

7. Samsam wants to know if he wants a boy or girl.  Yes   No

Circle the picture.

8. What do the colors pink and blue mean?

Sentence Practice

Part 1: Trace the long *u: u_e, ue, ew* words. Copy each sentence.

true	blue	news	clue	rule	few
true	blue	new	cute	due	

1. Samsam calls her husband, Ahmed, with the news.

   Samsam calls her husband, Ahmed, with the news.

2. "What's new?" Ahmed asks.

   _____

3. "I'll give you a clue," Samsam says.

   _____

4. "What's cute and little and wears pink or blue?"

   _____

5. Ahmed doesn't know the American rule for pink or blue.

   _____

6. "I'm pregnant and due in a few months!" Samsam says.

   _____

7. "Is that true?" Ahmed asks, surprised.

   _____

8. "Yes, it's true."

   _____

9. "What do you want, pink or blue?"

   _____

10. What do the colors pink and blue mean?

    _____

Part 2: Trace the sight words. Copy each sentence.

mean	give	husband	know	says
want	it's	what's	asks	little

1. Samsam calls her husband, Ahmed, with the news.

   Samsam calls her husband, Ahmed, with the news.

2. "What's new?" Ahmed asks.

   _____

3. "I'll give you a clue," Samsam says.

   _____

4. "What's cute and little and wears pink or blue?"

   _____

5. Ahmed doesn't know the American rule for pink or blue.

   _____

6. "I'm pregnant and due in a few months!" Samsam says.

   _____

7. "Is that true?" Ahmed asks, surprised.

   _____

8. "Yes, it's true."

   _____

9. "What do you want, pink or blue?"

   _____

10. What do the colors pink and blue mean?

    _____

Listening Quizzes
Part 1: Letter Sounds: Listen and write the missing letters.

1. cl_____

2. bl_____

3. n_____

4. c_____t_____

5. r_____l_____

6. f_____

7. _____ue

8. _____ew

9. _____ew

10. _____ue

11. _____u_____e

12. _____u_____e

Part 2: Word Families: Listen and write the long *u: ew, ue,* or *u_e* words.

1. _____

2. _____

3._____

4. _____

5. _____

6. _____

Part 3: Sound Match: Listen and circle the words you hear.

1. rail   rule   real

2. cut   cute   coat

3. tray   tree   true

4. due   die   day

5. knee   knew   know

6. flew   few   fly

Part 4: Sight Words: Listen and write the sight words.

1. _____

2. _____

3. _____

4. _____

5. _____

6. _____

7. _____

8. _____

9. _____

10. _____

Part 5: Dictation: Listen and complete the sentences.

1. Samsam calls her _____, Ahmed, with the _____.

2. "I'll _____ you a _____," Samsam says.

3. "What's _____ and _____ and wears pink
   or blue?"

4. "I'm pregnant and _____ in a _____ months!"
   Samsam says.

5. "Is that _____?" Ahmed _____, surprised.

6. "Yes, _____ _____."

7. "What do you _____, pink or _____?"

8. What do the colors pink and _____ _____?

Answer Key

Lesson 1: Apartment Problems

Reading Comprehension

1. No
2. Yes
3. Yes
4. Yes
5. No
6. No
7. Yes

Listening Quizzes

Part 1: Letter Sounds

1. m<u>i</u>ce
2. r<u>i</u>ce
3. t<u>i</u>me
4. wh<u>i</u>le
5. t<u>i</u>red
6. n<u>i</u>ce
7. t<u>i</u>me
8. n<u>i</u>ce
9. l<u>i</u>ke
10. wr<u>i</u>te
11. m<u>i</u>ce
12. p<u>i</u>pes

Part 2: Word Families

1. white
2. lime
3. bike
4. price
5. dime
6. kite

Part 3: Sound Match

1. <u>mice</u>   miss   mess

2. Tim   <u>time</u>   team
3. will   <u>while</u>   well
4. <u>fine</u>   fin   fan
5. lake   <u>like</u>   lick
6. Russ   race   <u>rice</u>

Part 4: Sight Words

1. apartment
2. washing
3. problems
4. running
5. maybe
6. broken
7. about
8. find
9. what
10. waiting

Part 5: Dictation

1. Samsam and Adam don't like their apartment.
2. It is in a nice location, but it has many problems.
3. Samsam is cooking rice, but the stove is broken.
4. Adam is washing dishes, but the pipes are leaking.
5. They told their landlord about the problems a while ago.
6. They are tired of waiting for him.
7. Maybe they will write a letter of complaint.
8. What will Samsam and Adam decide to do?

Lesson 2: Apartment Search

Reading Comprehension

1. No
2. Yes
3. No
4. No
5. No
6. No
7. Yes

Listening Quizzes
Part 1: Letter Sounds

1. m<u>igh</u>t
2. l<u>igh</u>t
3. s<u>igh</u>t
4. r<u>igh</u>t
5. h<u>igh</u>
6. f<u>igh</u>t
7. <u>r</u>igh<u>t</u>
8. <u>l</u>igh<u>t</u>
9. <u>brigh</u>t
10. <u>high</u>
11. <u>night</u>
12. <u>right</u>

Part 2: Word Families

1. sigh
2. tight
3. flight
4. light
5. night
6. bright

Part 3: Sound Match

1. mitt   <u>might</u>   mat
2. <u>sight</u>   sat   sit
3. fat   feet   <u>fight</u>
4. <u>light</u>   lit   let
5. say   <u>sigh</u>   see
6. rate   wrote   <u>right</u>

Part 4: Sight Words

1. appointment
2. landlord
3. bedroom
4. price
5. most
6. next
7. newspaper
8. there is
9. there are
10. welcome

Part 5: Dictation

1. Samsam and Adam decided not to fight their landlord.
2. Right now, they are looking at ads in the newspaper.
3. "This two bedroom looks all right," Samsam says.
4. "Let's make an appointment to see it tonight," Adam agrees.
5. The apartment is a welcome sight.
6. There are two large bedrooms that are clean and bright.
7. The utilities are included, and the price is right.
8. What might Samsam and Adam do next?

Lesson 3: Samsam's Doctor's Appointment

Reading Comprehension

1. Yes
2. Yes
3. No
4. Yes
5. Yes
6. No
7. No

Listening Quizzes
Part 1: Letter Sounds

1. m<u>oa</u>n
2. c<u>oa</u>t
3. kn<u>ow</u>
4. sh<u>ow</u>
5. g<u>oa</u>t
6. bel<u>ow</u>
7. <u>thr</u>ow
8. <u>b</u>oat
9. <u>c</u>oat
10. <u>s</u>how
11. goa<u>t</u>
12. <u>kn</u>ow

Part 2: Word Families

1. throat
2. loan
3. low
4. blow
5. float
6. grow

Part 3: Sound Match

1. <u>moan</u>   man   mean
2. cat   <u>coat</u>   cut
3. got   <u>goat</u>   get
4. she   shy   <u>show</u>
5. <u>know</u>   knee   not
6. <u>low</u>   lie   lay

Part 4: Sight Words

1. appointment
2. doctor
3. clinic
4. results
5. feels
6. form
7. wakes up
8. signs
9. wrong
10. ate

Part 5: Dictation

1. Samsam wakes up with a moan.
2. She throws up the goat meat she ate last night.
3. At her appointment, she shows her insurance card.
4. She fills out each row on the medical history form.
5. She signs her name below.
6. Then the doctor wants to know about her symptoms.
7. "I think I know what's wrong," the doctor says.
8. What will Samsam's test results show?

Lesson 4: Doctor's Orders
Reading Comprehension
1. Yes
2. Yes
3. No
4. Yes
5. No
6. No
7. No

Listening Quizzes
Part 1: Letter Sounds
1. m<u>or</u>e
2. sh<u>ow</u>s
3. h<u>o</u>p<u>e</u>
4. h<u>o</u>me
5. sm<u>o</u>ke
6. d<u>o</u>se
7. <u>hope</u>
8. <u>home</u>
9. <u>ph</u>one
10. <u>sh</u>ows
11. <u>no</u>te
12. <u>sm</u>oke

Part 2: Word Families
1. shore
2. rope
3. bone
4. broke
5. stone
6. store

Part 3: Sound Match
1. <u>home</u>   him   ham
2. <u>know</u>   knee   knew
3. <u>phone</u>   fun   fan
4. she   shy   <u>show</u>
5. <u>note</u>   night   not
6. <u>hope</u>   hop   hip

Part 4: Sight Words
1. who
2. once
3. gives
4. results
5. feels
6. should
7. shouldn't
8. doesn't
9. months
10. can't

Part 5: Dictation
1. The doctor shows Samsam the test results.
2. Samsam doesn't feel as sick anymore.
3. "You'll feel sick a couple more months," the doctor says.
4. "You should eat more fruits and vegetables."
5. "You shouldn't smoke or drink alcohol or coffee."
6. "You should take one dose once a day," she says.
7. Samsam can't wait to get home to use the phone.
8. Who will she call on the phone?

Lesson 5: Samsam's Surprise
Reading Comprehension
1. No
2. Yes
3. No
4. Yes
5. Yes
6. Yes
7. Yes

Listening Quizzes
Part 1: Letter Sounds
1. cl<u>ue</u>
2. bl<u>ue</u>
3. n<u>ew</u>
4. c<u>u</u>te
5. r<u>u</u>le
6. <u>f</u>ew
7. <u>b</u>lue
8. <u>n</u>ew
9. <u>f</u>ew
10. <u>t</u>rue
11. c<u>u</u>te
12. r<u>u</u>le

Part 2: Word Families
1. mute
2. glue
3. chew
4. flute
5. grew
6. clue

Part 3: Sound Match
1. rail   <u>rule</u>   real
2. cut   <u>cute</u>   coat
3. tray   tree   <u>true</u>
4. <u>due</u>   die   day
5. knee   <u>knew</u>   know
6. flew   <u>few</u>   fly

Part 4: Sight Words
1. little
2. what's
3. it's
4. husband
5. want
6. give
7. know
8. mean
9. says
10. asks

Part 5: Dictation
1. Samsam calls her husband, Ahmed, with the news.
2. "I'll give you a clue," Samsam says.
3. "What's cute and little and wears pink or blue?"
4. "I'm pregnant and due in a few months!" Samsam says.
5. "Is that true?" Ahmed asks, surprised.
6. "Yes, it's true."
7. "What do you want, pink or blue?"
8. What do the colors pink and blue mean?